(c) 2021

I want to dedicate this book to my mother Dollie R. Edwards for the many years of love and support. To my high school chorus teacher Sabra Shores for seeing the gift inside of me. To Loreida Burch Austin for accompanying me on the piano that day. Finally, I want to thank Norah Cowan for introducing me to the student that inspired this book. Thank you!

Editors

R. Zoe Johnson
Julia Flattes
Amy Barringer

KEVIN TURNS FEAR INTO FEAT

WRITTEN BY KEVIN B. EDWARDS

"Kevin, the Black History Celebration will be tomorrow, and I want you to perform a song on the program. I have already selected a song I think would be a great fit for your voice. Our student pianist, Lori, will accompany you."

"Lori," Ms. Shores said, "I will give you a copy of the sheet music today to prepare for tomorrow."

"I already know how to play the song, and it would be an honor to accompany Kevin," Lori replied with a huge smile.

"Kevin, come around the piano and let's test the song to see if, indeed, it will display your vocal ability," said Ms. Shores.

"Will the whole school be there?" asked Kevin with a scared look on his face.

"Yes! The entire school will be in the gym, but I am most certain you can do this," replied Ms. Shores.

"Ms. Shores, I am a-fr-aid to sing for that many people. I have never s-ung for anyone at our school," sputtered Kevin, nervous that kids might laugh at him.

"I know you can do it. You have an outstanding voice and God will be with you. We will rehearse until you know the song perfectly before leaving school today," reassured Ms. Shores.

"Kevin, do you remember when we sang the Andre Crouch song 'I Don't Know Why Jesus Loved Me' a few days ago?" asked Ms. Shores.

"Yes, I remember singing that song, but I'm not sure if I can remember all the words to sing it tomorrow," replied Kevin.

"I just want you to learn the structure of the song. You will use sheet music for the lyrics. I will have a music stand out front for you to place the sheet music on," said Ms. Shores.

Lori began to play the music on the piano and Kevin closed his eyes and began to add his melodious voice to the piano accompaniment.

"See, I knew you could sing this song beautifully. You will be awesome tomorrow!" Ms. Shores encouraged him with a huge smile.

"I hope I am not booed off the stage," worried Kevin.

"You won't be booed; I am sure of that. You are a talented young man." replied Ms. Shores.

That evening, Kevin came home from school terrified about what he would face the next day at school. As a small child, he never felt he fit in with the other kids. He was constantly bullied at home by the neighborhood kids and at school by his peers. Kevin lacked confidence; however, little did he know... this performance was about to give him all the confidence he needed for a lifetime.

"How am I going to get up in front of all of those people tomorrow and sing when they don't even like me?" Kevin asked himself.

"Mom, the Chorus teacher at school asked me to sing for the entire school tomorrow, and I am scared," said Kevin with a petrified look on his face.

"Kevin, you are very well capable of getting up there and singing to that crowd. Just close your eyes and sing from your heart, just like at church. Just remember when you open your eyes, just look above the crowd instead of directly at them and that will help you not to be afraid of them," replied Mom.

Kevin was restless the entire night. He did not sleep well, worried about the performance the next day. Kevin tossed and turned in his bed all night, trembling underneath his sheets. As time went by, the next morning came, and it was time for school. Kevin was so nervous, that he could not eat breakfast. He dreaded the day's events. However, it would soon be over.

"God, please help me not to be afraid today. Please don't allow anyone to laugh at me or yell mean things," prayed Kevin.

"Good Morning Kevin! You will do great today at the assembly. Remember everything I told you last night. Have an awesome day at school! " said his mom as she gave him a big hug.

"Thank you mom!" replied Kevin as he opened the door and left to catch the school bus.

At 9:30 a.m. Kevin was instructed by his chorus teacher to head to the gym to get into place for the assembly. While sitting there, Kevin watched the students, faculty and staff pack the gym seats. His nerves were on overdrive waiting to see the response of the crowd. The principal made his remarks, the program coordinator spoke, and Kevin was next to sing. He heard his name called and he slowly began to get out of his seat to walk to the podium.

As Kevin began to walk to the podium, he imagined he would hear noises coming from the crowd, but it was completely silent as he approached the stage to sing.

Everyone was surprised to see Kevin on stage that day. A few students from his church had heard him, but most were about to hear him for the first time. As he got out of his seat, much of the fear had left him, and a great courage entered his body. He could feel something helping him to stand in front of the crowd. Kevin wondered what it was.

He got into place, and Lori nodded that she was about to start playing the music. He didn't have to worry about remembering his lyrics because they were right in front of him. Lori played the introduction of the song and he began to sing the first note.

To his surprise, no one uttered a sound the entire time he sang. Had he mesmerized the entire audience? Maybe they were just shocked that he could actually sing. As he held the last note of the song, he heard clapping from the audience. He could have had a standing ovation, but he was too afraid to look. Had they actually enjoyed listening to him?

All of his childhood, Kevin had felt rejected and a misfit, but today he was being saluted with applause. This was the best feeling he had ever experienced in his life!

The assembly lasted for about an hour and then all students started returning to class. Kevin walked away from the gym and wanted to hurry back to his classroom because he really was afraid of negative comments. To his surprise, he was stopped by the crowd saying, "You have a beautiful voice! You can sing! You are gifted! What a blessing you were!"

Students and teachers that had never spoken to him, stopped him and complimented his performance. From that day until the day he graduated from high school, he was known around the school as "the boy that sings with an outstanding voice."

After that performance, Kevin was asked to sing at many school functions including spring concerts, competitions, proms, and high school graduation services. He and another student, Annie Pearl Jenkins, won second place in a school competition. His ability to sing shed a new light on him as a student. His classmates admired what he did, and it caused the bullies to view him in a different way from that day forward.

Kevin pushed through his insecurities and his lack of self-confidence and found that he was indeed self-reliant. Every young person that is struggling with low self-esteem should find that one gift that has been placed inside of them and use it as a way to build their confidence. Kevin's musical gift has given him the self-assurance he needs to perform before many people here in the USA and even in other countries. A day of fear turned into a day of feat.

About the Author

Kevin B. Edwards is a graduate of Troy University in Dothan, Alabama with a B.S. Degree in Psychology. This is Kevin's first children's book. Kevin can be reached via website www.kevinbedwards.com

kevinbedwards1382@gmail.com

Facebook: Kevin Edwards

Instagram: kevinedwards9822

Twitter: @Kevinsings

About the Illustrator

George Franco is a prolific self-taught artist.
He has strong faith in the Lord and loves his Family and pets. It is his dream to one day teach and motivate the younger generation to find their paths in life. He is from Manila, Philippines.
George can be reached via website georgefrancoart.weebly.com

georgefrancoart@gmail.com

Facebook: George Franco